A Fish for Lunch

Tasha Pym

Illustrated by Mark Oliver

I wish I had a fish for lunch.

3

That is a frog.

That is not a fish!

That is a shell.

That is not a fish!

That is a ship.

That is not a fish!

That is a duck. Yuk!

I wish I had a fish to munch.

I wish I had a fish to crunch . . .

A big big fish for lunch!

LANDMARKS OF THE WORLD

Written by Helen Chapman

Contents

Collins

What is a landmark?

A landmark is a well-known object or feature of a place that is easy to see and recognise.

It helps people to understand where they are in the world.

Within each of Earth's seven **continents** are man-made landmarks. Let's visit some of them!

Africa

This pyramid is a **tomb** for a dead ruler called a pharaoh.

It is the largest pyramid ever built.

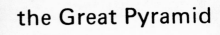

the Great Pyramid

4

This statue, with a lion's body and a man's head, guards the **tomb**.

the Great Sphinx

Antarctica

Halley 6 Research Station

Although Antarctica is almost completely covered by ice, scientists work here all year round.

Their research station is made up of eight buildings called modules.

Landmark fact!

Each module is on skis and can easily be pulled to a different place.

Asia

Burj Khalifa, Dubai, United Arab Emirates

The world's tallest building reaches into the sky above the desert city of Dubai.

Inside there are homes, offices, shops, a hotel and swimming pools.

8

Landmark fact!

The weight of the concrete
used in the Burj Khalifa
is the same as
100,000 elephants!

Australia

Is this a sculpture or a building?
It's both!

The building is used for performing
arts such as **opera**, concerts,
plays and dances.

10

Landmark fact!

Over one million tiles
cover the sail-shaped roof.

Europe

Edinburgh Castle, Scotland sits upon a **dormant** volcano. Over one million people visit the castle every year.

The Walled City of Derry, Northern Ireland is Ireland's only city which is completely surrounded by a wall. Many people live and work here.

The London Eye, England is one of the world's tallest viewing wheels. Visitors can see for around 40 kilometres from the top of the wheel.

Dinorwig Power Station, Wales makes electricity deep inside Europe's largest man-made **cavern**.

inside the power station

13

Europe

The Hundertwasser House, Vienna, Austria

This famous building brings nature and architecture together.

The front is a patchwork of bright colours, curves and uneven shapes.

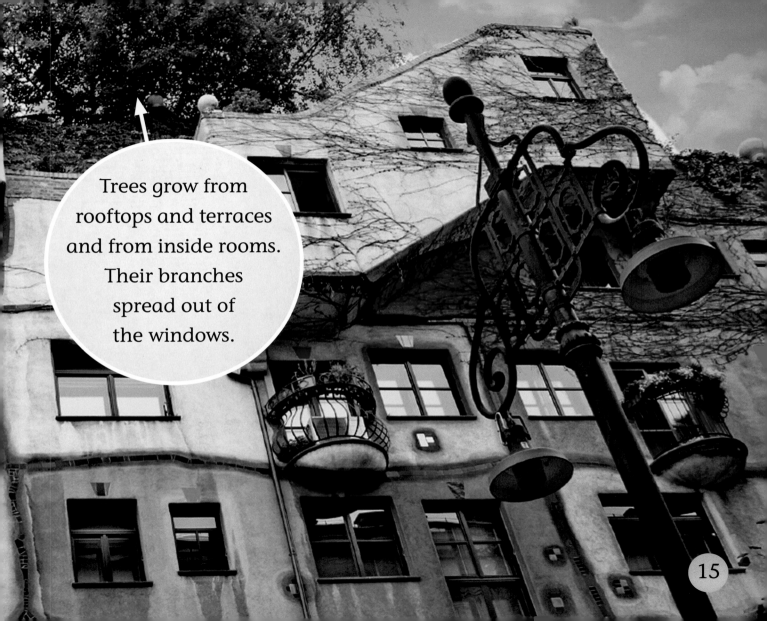

Trees grow from rooftops and terraces and from inside rooms. Their branches spread out of the windows.

15

Europe

Colosseum, Rome, Italy

Around 2,000 years ago, the world's largest **amphitheatre** held **gladiator** battles and wild animal fights.

Landmark fact!

The inside of the Colosseum could be flooded for make-believe water battles.

North America

Statue of Liberty, New York City

This statue of a lady was a gift of friendship from the people of France. She is a **symbol** of freedom and **democracy**. This statue welcomes people coming to live in, or visit, America.

Lady Liberty was often the first thing people saw as they arrived in America by boat.

Landmark fact!

Liberty's torch is covered with thin sheets of gold.

South America

Machu Picchu, Cusco Region, Peru

This ancient city was built on top of a mountain at an enormous 2,720 metres above sea level. It was forgotten for hundreds of years until 1911.

Landmark fact!

Machu Picchu was built by lots of people carrying very heavy stones without using any machinery or animals.

Glossary

amphitheatre   a large building with seats rising in curved rows around an open space

cavern   a large cave, often found underground

continents   the main landmasses of Earth

democracy   government by the people

dormant   a volcano that has not erupted in a long time but could erupt in the future

gladiator   professional fighter or slave who entertained the public by battling to the death

opera   a play where all parts are sung to music

symbol   an object that stands for something else

tomb   a building above or below the ground in which a dead body is kept

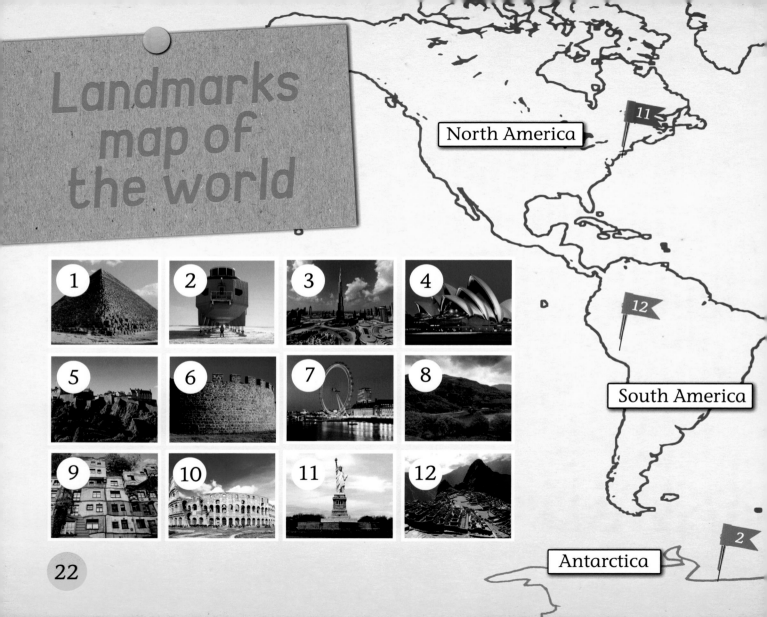

Landmarks map of the world

North America

South America

Antarctica

11

12

2

1
2
3
4
5
6
7
8
9
10
11
12

22

Europe

Asia

Africa

Australia

23

Ideas for reading

Written by Clare Dowdall, PhD
Lecturer and Primary Literacy Consultant

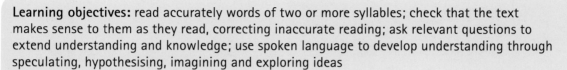

Learning objectives: read accurately words of two or more syllables; check that the text makes sense to them as they read, correcting inaccurate reading; ask relevant questions to extend understanding and knowledge; use spoken language to develop understanding through speculating, hypothesising, imagining and exploring ideas

Curriculum links: Geography

Interest words: ampitheatre, cavern, continent, democracy, dormant, gladiator, opera, symbol, tomb

Resources: pens and paper, globe, map of the world, ICT

Word count: 403

Getting started

- Read the title of the book aloud. Ask children to explain what the word *Landmarks* means. Help them to notice that the word is made of two syllables, which are separate words, and that this helps to understand what the word means.

- Look at the images on the front and back covers. Ask children to name any landmarks that they recognise and to suggest any others that they may know.

- Read the contents together. Discuss how the book is organised, e.g. by continent. If necessary, introduce children to the idea that these headings are all continents of the world.